THIS WALKER BOOK BELONGS TO:

_____

_____

_____

_____

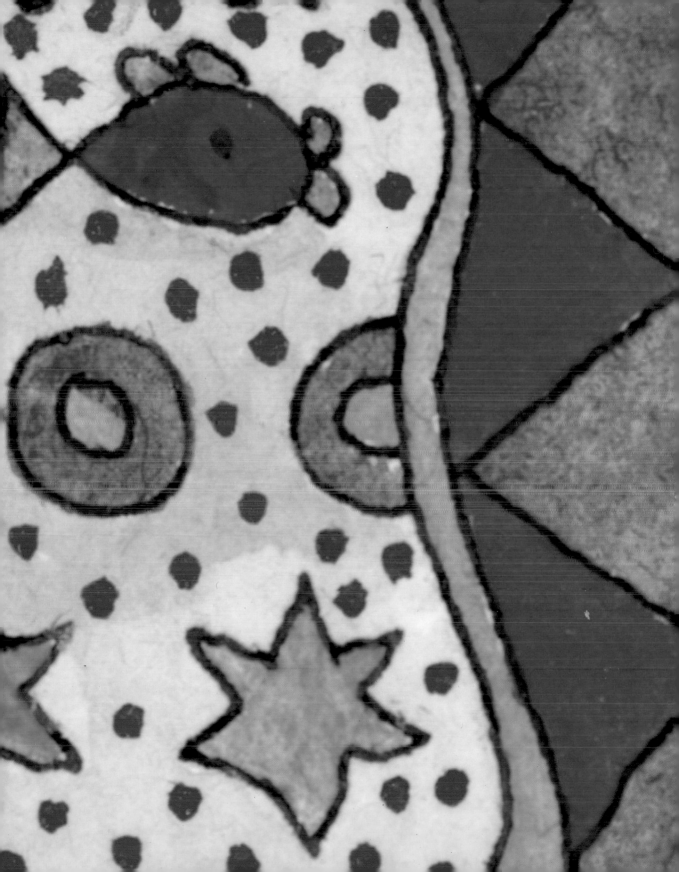

For Pepper and Colin

First published 1990
by Walker Books Ltd
87 Vauxhall Walk
London SE11 5HJ

This edition published 1998

2 4 6 8 10 9 7 5 3 1

Printed in Hong Kong

British Library Cataloguing in Publication Data
A catalogue record for this book is
available from the British Library.

ISBN 0-7445-6060-8

JOSEPH AND HIS
MAGNIFICENT COAT
OF MANY COLOURS

Written and illustrated by

Marcia Williams

WALKER BOOKS
AND SUBSIDIARIES
LONDON • BOSTON • SYDNEY

There once lived, in the land of Canaan,

a farmer called Jacob.

Jacob had twelve fine sons,

but the one he loved best was Joseph.

HAPPY 17th BIRTHDAY

Jacob gave Joseph a magnificent coat of many colours,

In Joseph's first dream,

he and his brothers were binding corn.

In this dream, Joseph's sheaf rose and stood upright

and his brothers' sheaves bowed down before it.

In Joseph's second dream

the sun, the moon and eleven stars

bowed down before him as though he were king.

Joseph's father believed the dreams meant

that Joseph would become a great ruler.

But one of the brothers, named Reuben,

persuaded the others not to kill Joseph.

Instead, they stripped off his magnificent coat

and cast him into a pit.

Then, at midday, as the brothers sat down to eat,

they saw a company of Ishmaelites ride over the hill,

their camels loaded with spices to sell in Egypt.

The brothers decided to sell Joseph to the travellers

in exchange for a bag of silver.

Then they dipped Joseph's beautiful coat in blood,

and returned home to their father.

Jacob was heartbroken when he saw the coat.

Believing that Joseph had been killed by wild beasts,

he put on sackcloth and mourned his favourite son.

For two years Joseph languished in prison.

The other prisoners liked and respected him,

for he was a wise interpreter of their dreams.

But for Joseph it was a sad and lonely time.

sat puzzling over two strange dreams.

His wise man could not fathom their meaning,

so Joseph was brought out of prison

and asked to interpret them.

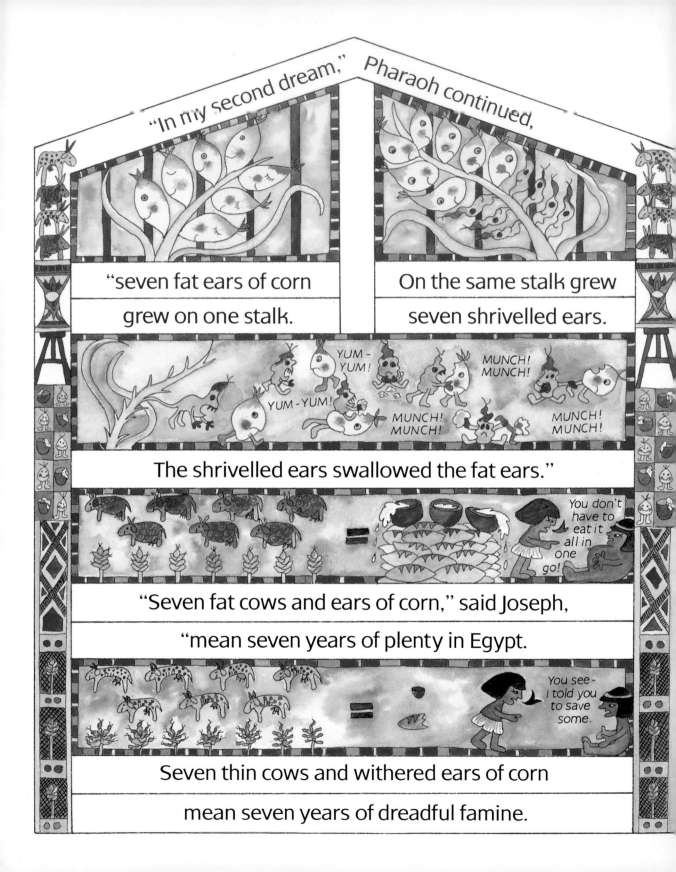

Pharaoh was so impressed by Joseph's wisdom

that he put him in charge of storing food.

He gave Joseph his ring and a gold chain,

some fine clothes and a splendid chariot.

Joseph became governor of all Egypt.

Joseph pretended to think his brothers were spies,

for he wished to see if they were still evil.

He threatened to enslave Benjamin, the youngest.

His brothers were distraught —

losing Benjamin would break their father's heart.

The brothers pleaded with Joseph to enslave

them instead, and set Benjamin free.

Joseph saw then that his brothers had changed.

He knew that they loved Benjamin and their father

and would give their lives for them.

MORE WALKER PAPERBACKS
For You to Enjoy

Other retellings by Marcia Williams

THE AMAZING STORY OF NOAH'S ARK

The amazing story of Noah and his ark is one of the world's greatest and best-loved tales.
Bright comic-strip illustrations and a simple text bring this favourite
Old Testament story to life for young children.

"Friendly, lively and intricate… Beautifully coloured borders."
The Observer

0-7445-6058-6   £4.99

JONAH AND THE WHALE

When Jonah disobeys God, he finds himself in the belly of an enormous whale!
More comic-strip Bible story fun.

"What makes Marcia Williams' version of the story so absorbing are the
wonderfully detailed and beautiful illustrations…
A picture book full of life and colour." *Child Education*

0-7445-6059-4   £4.99

THE ILIAD AND THE ODYSSEY

The Iliad tells the story of the war between the Greeks and the Trojans.
The Odyssey depicts the perilous voyage home of the Greek warrior, Odysseus.

"A big, beautifully produced book, telling the stories in irresistibly detailed
comic-strip form… Elegant, intelligent, funny, dramatic and totally absorbing;
the perfect start to an early familiarity with Homer." *The Guardian*

0-7445-5430-6   £5.99

Walker Paperbacks are available from most booksellers, or by post from B.B.C.S., P.O. Box 941, Hull, North Humberside HU1 3YQ
24 hour telephone credit card line 01482 224626

To order, send: Title, author, ISBN number and price for each book ordered, your full name and address,
cheque or postal order payable to BBCS for the total amount and allow the following for postage and packing:
UK and BFPO: £1.00 for the first book, and 50p for each additional book to a maximum of £3.50.
Overseas and Eire: £2.00 for the first book, £1.00 for the second and 50p for each additional book.

Prices and availability are subject to change without notice.